LOTTE FORDE

COLOR THE FOREST

COLORING BOOK

FANTASTICAL JOURNEY INTO THE WORLD OF TREES

BOOK 2 IN THE COLOR BOOK SERIES

Get your FREE Coloring Book

Looking for more to color?

This free coloring book is available to everybody who signs up to my newsletter. Just scan the QR code and it will take you straight to my website. Just follow the steps. Or just visit:

LotteForde.com

You can unsubscribe anytime. You still get the book.

There is happiness in coloring.

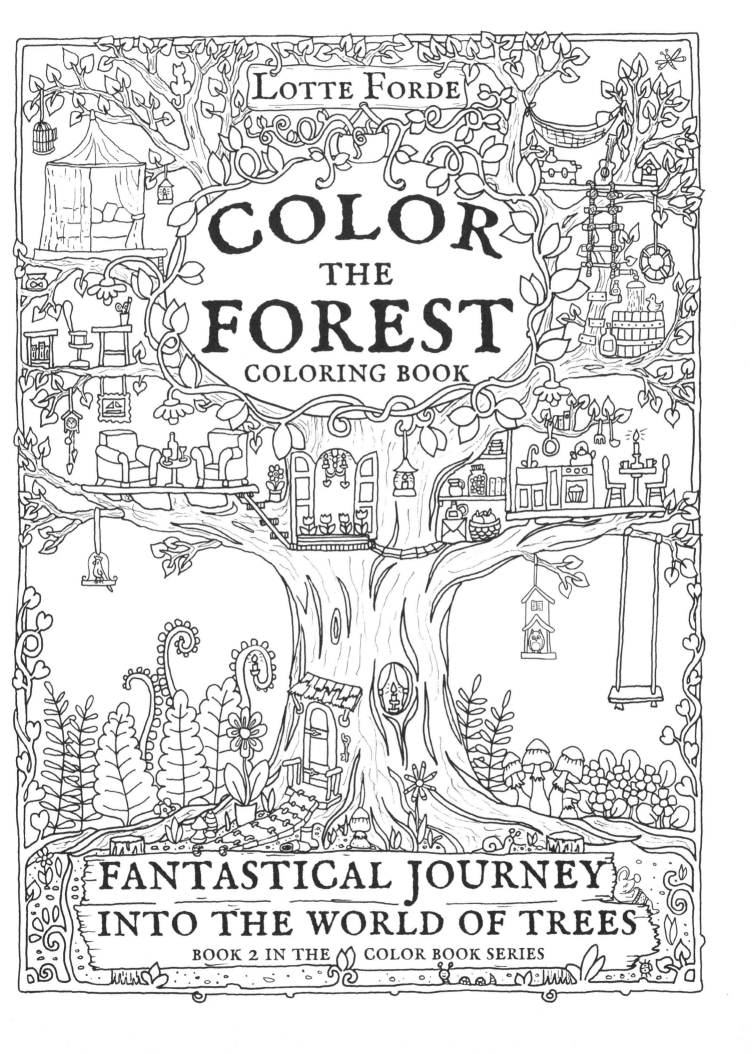

This book
belongs to:

Welcome To Color The Forest

Trees, mushrooms, flowers, ferns, creepers, crawlies and magical creatures can be found in the illustrations of this second book in the Lotte Forde Color Book Series. Immerse yourself in the fantasy world of tree houses, burrows, mushroom homes and more. Size doesn't matter. You can find a house in the smallest flower bud or on the tallest tree.

Find your favorite home in the forest and bring it to life with your color. I hope you have as much fun discovering and coloring this new world as I had dreaming it up and drawing it.

Lotte

Tips on Coloring:

You will find color test pages a few times throughout the book.

Test pages come in handy if you want to try out different coloring techniques. Here you can test your pens or pencils. Instead of leaving the pages blank they have simple patterns and illustrations.

When coloring, a lot of people find colored pencils are best. You can blend and mix your colors and there is no wet ink bleeding into the paper.

I deliberately left the reverse side of all the coloring pages blank. This is to avoid any coloring of the previous page shining or leaking through to the other side. Each drawing has it's own page to avoid messing up other drawings.

It is a good idea to place a separate blank piece of paper behind the page you are working on. If you use pens or liquid inks to color the spare paper will help prevent any leaky color appearing on the next drawing in the book.

An extra paper can also avoid dents appearing on the next page. This may happen especially when applying pressure with your pencil as you work.

Color Palette Test Page

(or just tree houses if you don't need to test your colors)

Shroom Town

Two Shrooms

Fairy Home

Echinacea Homes

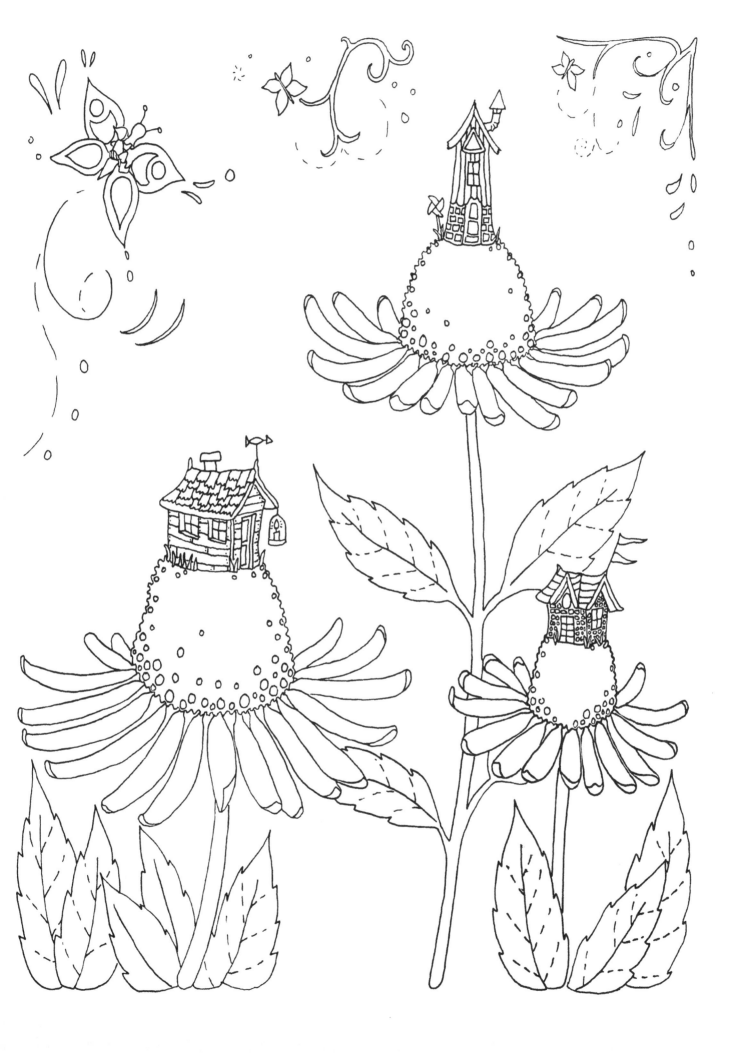

The Burrow

Forest Circle

The Climbing Tree

Tree Lines

Island Escape

The Shroom Stack Shack

Daisy Chain

Offsprings

Offsprings

Color Palette Test Page

Flower-Ring

Willow Hollow

Ground Level

The Bird's Home

The Mushroom Home

Fairy Lights

Flower Retreat

Home Tree

Rose's Home

The Evergreens

Flying Fun

Playful Flowers

Fast Lane

Your Second Set of Drawings
Start Here:

This book comes with a second set
of illustrations. They are the same
wonderful drawings you've enjoyed
so far, a second time around. You
can give each drawing another go.
Try out something completely
different, use new techniques, media
and colors, have fun!

Lotte

Shroom Town

Two Shrooms

Fairy Home

Echinacea Homes

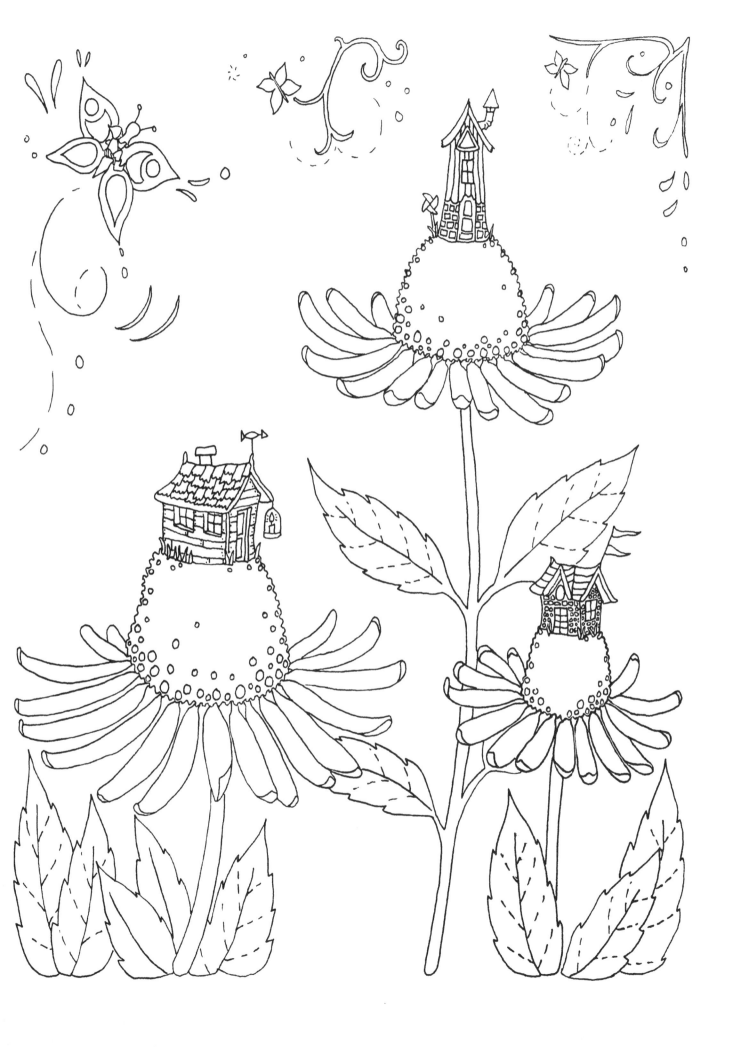

The Burrow

Forest Circle

The Climbing Tree

Tree Lines

Island Escape

The Shroom Stack Shack

Daisy Chain

Offsprings

Color Palette Test Page

Flower-Ring

Ground Level

The Bird's Home

The Mushroom Home

Fairy Lights

Flower Retreat

Home Tree

Rose's Home

The Evergreens

Playful Flowers

Fast Lane

Thank You

I hope you enjoyed Color The Forest.

Please share your coloring work with me and the world. For any social media posts you have featuring illustrations from this book please tag #ColorTheForestBook and #LotteForde so I can enjoy your work too! You can find me on social media:

Instagram: instagram.com/lotteforde

Twitter: twitter.com/lotteforde

Pinterest: pinterest.com/lotteforde

Look out for more coloring adventures by Lotte Forde. Subscribe to the newsletter and download the free coloring book - Color the World on my website.

lotteforde.com

As an independently published author I'm extremely grateful for any reviews of my books on Amazon.

This QR code will take you straight to the Amazon review page. Just scan the code and leave a review. Thank you.

About the Author:

Lotte Forde is an author and illustrator. Her illustrations are all hand drawn with pen and paper. The drawings are whimsical, playful and full of lovely detail. She creates fantastical worlds inspired by nature and the world around her. She lives with her husband in rural Ireland. They have a small garden with lots of beautiful flowers and a shed full of tools for tinkering in their spare time. Sometimes the neighbour's cat comes to visit.

lotteforde.com

More books by Lotte Forde:

Check out Book 1 in the Color Book Series by Lotte Forde

COLOR THE SKY
FANTASTICAL JOURNEY INTO THE CLOUDS

Just scan the QR code and it will take you straight to the product page on Amazon.com.

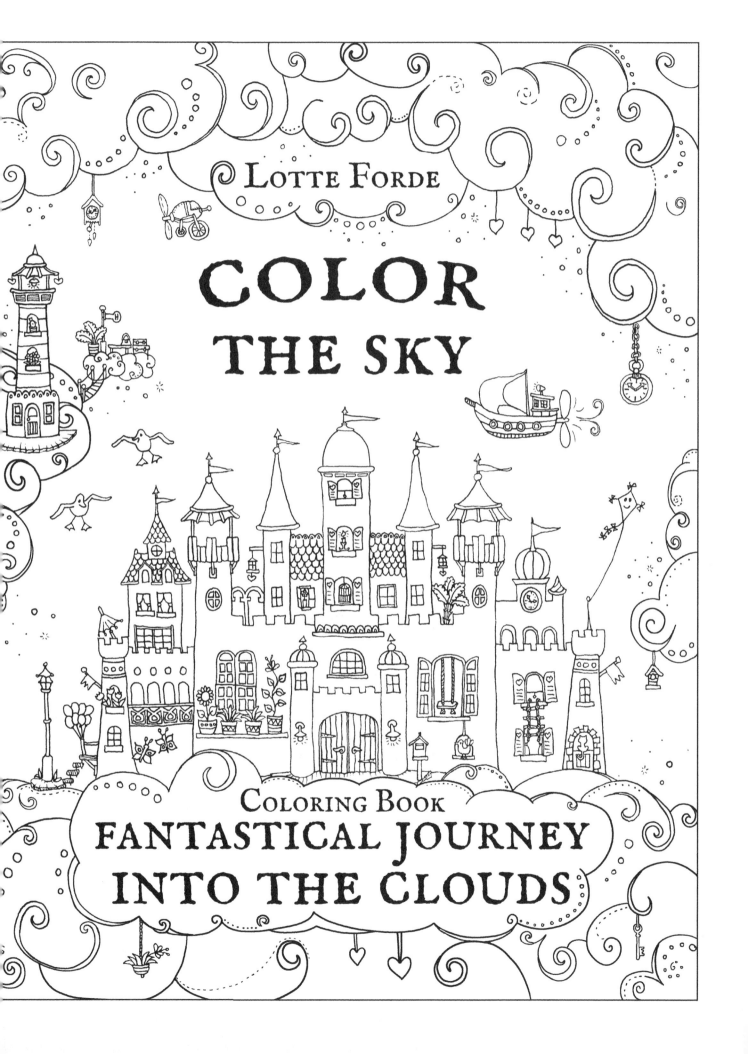

LOTTE FORDE

COLOR
THE SKY

COLORING BOOK
FANTASTICAL JOURNEY
INTO THE CLOUDS

Looking for more to color by Lotte Forde?

I now have a selection of the drawings from my books
as well as unique once of pieces available to buy
as PDF downloads on the

Lotte Forde Etsy Shop.

With a PDF you can print any of my illustrations on the media
of your choice, giving you even more options.

Why not browse for your all-time favourites or discover
something new illustrated by me. Just scan the QR code below
and the link will take you straight to the Lotte Forde Etsy shop.

Color Palette Test Page

Made in the USA
Monee, IL
13 March 2023

29763953R00066